SPECIAL THANKS: ANNA ANTHROPY, EZRA
BUTT, SEAN CHRISTENSEN, SEAN T COLLINS,
JULIA GFRÖRER, LILLY MOORE, AMBER SMITH
JEFF SMITH, SUZETTE SMITH, ZACK SOTO, +
FRANCOIS VIGNEAULT

DEDICATED TO THE COLVILLE STREET PATISSERIE
AND TO DAVID KANAGA

HAUNTER

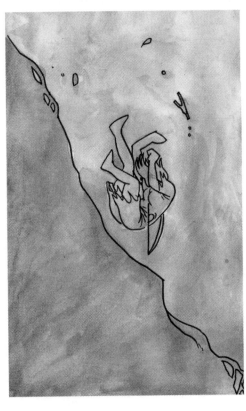

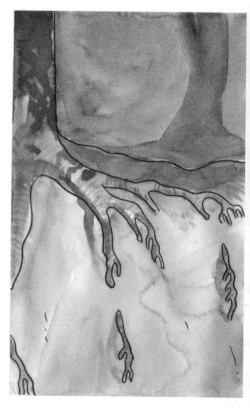

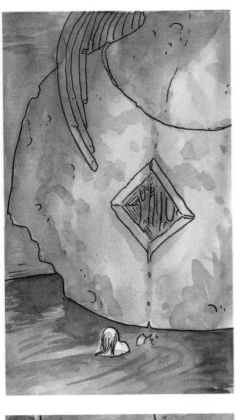

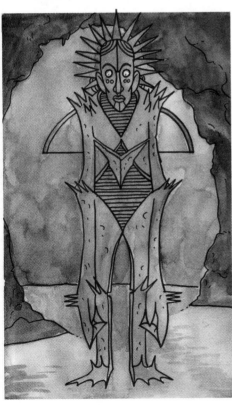

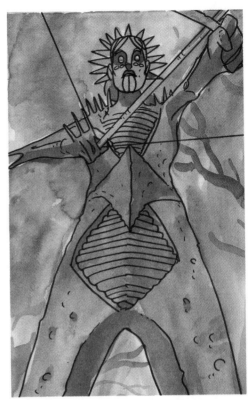

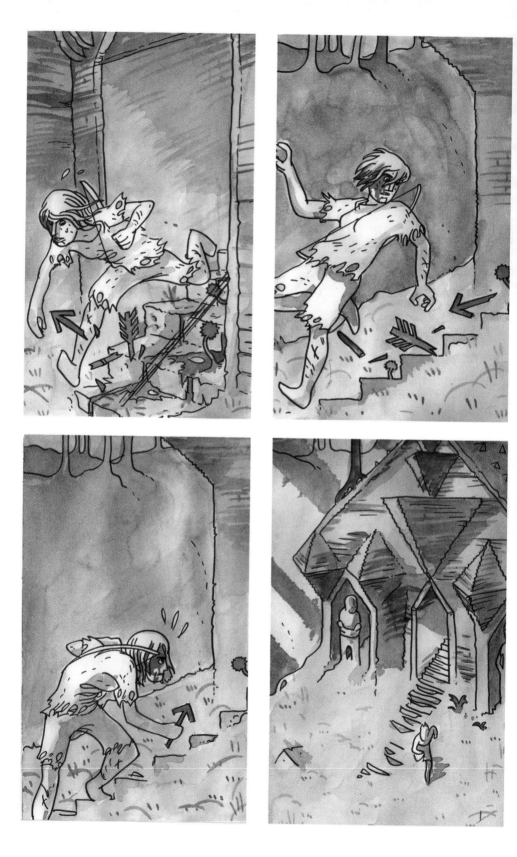

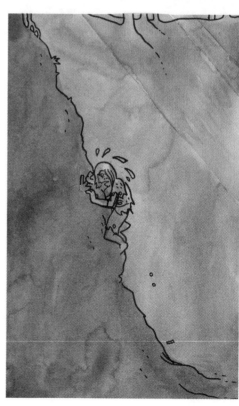

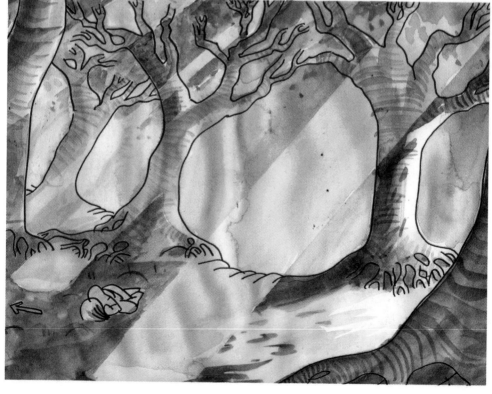

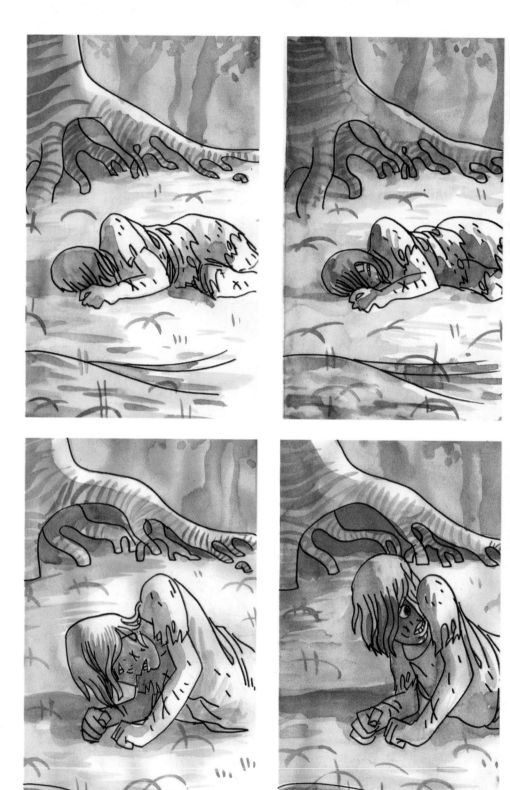

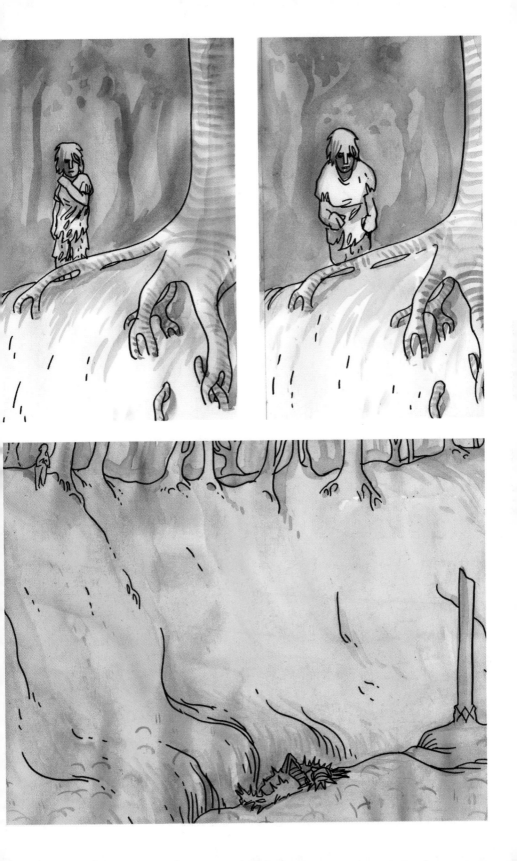

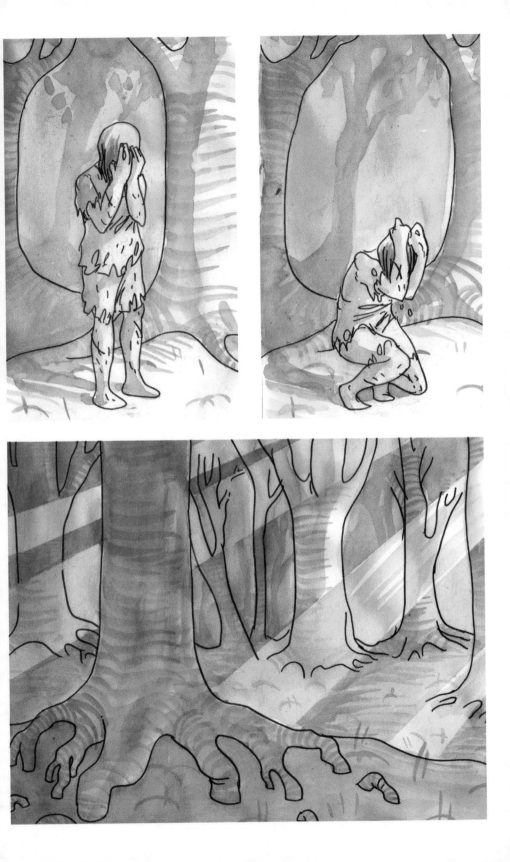

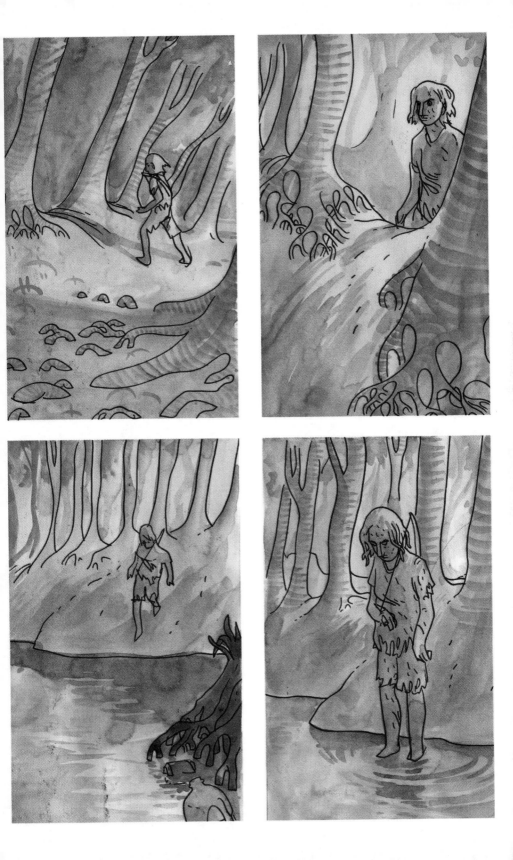

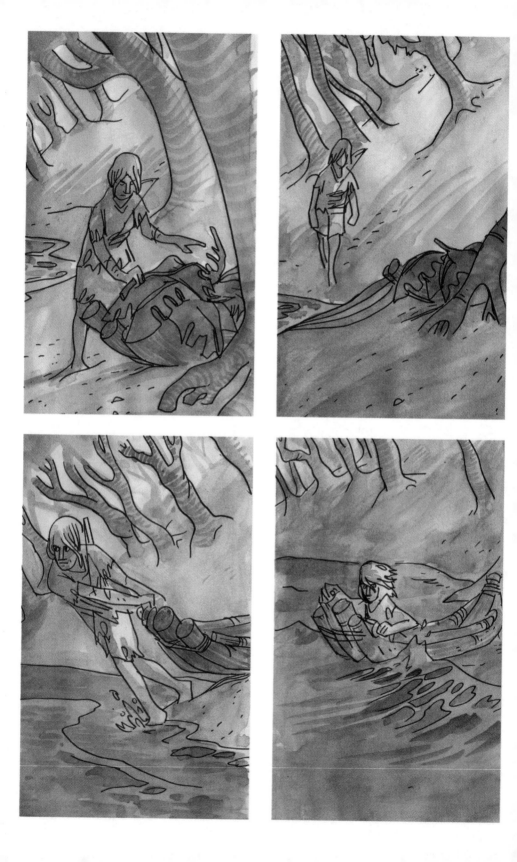